LEWY BODY DEMENTIA

Activities for the Family Caregiver
HOW TO ENGAGE, HOW TO LIVE

Endorsed by

National Council of Certified Dementia Practitioners

Scott Silknitter, Robert D. Brennan,
and Linda Redhead

Disclaimer

This book is for informational purposes only and is not intended as medical advice, diagnosis, or treatment. Always seek advice from a qualified physician about medical concerns, and do not disregard medical advice because of something you may read within this book. This book does not replace the need for diagnostic evaluation, ongoing physician care, and professional assessment of treatments. Every effort has been made to make this book as complete and helpful as possible. It is important, however, for this book to be used as a resource and idea-generating guide and not as an ultimate source for plan of care.

ISBN # 978-1-943285-15-0

Published by
R.O.S. Therapy Systems, L.L.C.
Greensboro, NC
888-352-9788
www.ROSTherapySystems.com

Foreword

From early in the disease course, most families affected by Lewy body dementia (LBD) find themselves on an unpredictable journey. And they have no roadmap to guide them. I know, because it happened in my family. Together, my father and I navigated LBD, sometimes getting lost and occasionally breaking down, until he reached the end of his road. There are definitely better ways to travel.

Activities for the Family Caregiver – Lewy Body Dementia by R.O.S. Therapy Systems offers help navigating everyday life with LBD. By integrating these proactive and person-centered care tips, caregivers may discover their confidence in their abilities growing. And the person with LBD may receive ongoing care that reflects appreciation for their individuality as a person.

LBD affects the primary caregiver nearly as much as the person diagnosed, yet typically the caregiver places their needs last. It is my hope that the readers of *Activities for the Family Caregiver – Lewy Body Dementia* take heed of the lesson included within its pages, on the importance of placing their own needs on equal footing with the person for whom they provide care.

I know both my father and I would have benefited from this book, as will countless LBD families who read it in the years to come.

—Angela Taylor, Director of Programs, Lewy Body Dementia Association

Activities for the Family Caregiver— Lewy Body Dementia

Like all of the forms of dementia that we have written about, Lewy body dementia has some unique characteristics that can be challenging for all family caregivers. We have written this book as a simple guide to help with the "How To's" of engaging your loved one.

Whether it is leisure activities or activities of daily living, I am on a mission to make sure that no family caregiver goes through what my family did in our 25-year fight with Dad's Parkinson's and dementia. For our Lewy body dementia book, we have accepted the assistance of Robert D. Brennan, RN, NHA, MS, CDP, and Linda Redhead, MS, ACC/EDU, who have been working in senior care for 60 years combined.

We have written this book in everyday language with real world examples and common sense suggestions for you to provide helpful information on engaging, caregiving, and activities of daily living.

We hope you find it useful and encourage you to have other family members and caregivers of your loved one read this in order to be consistent with approaches, verbal cues, physical assistance, and modifications that produce positive results.

From our family of caregivers to yours, please remember that you are not alone, and to never give up.

—Scott Silknitter, Founder of R.O.S. Therapy Systems, L.L.C.

Table of Contents

Family Members and Caregivers
that have read this book:

_____

_____

_____

_____

_____

_____

_____

_____

_____

_____

_____

Chapter 1

Lewy Body Dementia Overview

Lewy Body Dementia (LBD) may not be as well-known as other dementias, but it accounts for 20% of individuals with dementia worldwide.

As with any dementia, the more you are informed about Lewy body dementia, the better you can recognize the changes occurring in your loved one's world.

Lewy body dementia is caused by abnormal deposits of protein in the brain. These protein clumps are called "Lewy bodies." The clumping of this protein may cause the brain cells to work less effectively and eventually die. The Lewy bodies affect the normal chemicals of the brain leading to problems with movement, thinking, and behavior.

Lewy body dementia is a description for two known types of dementia:

1. Dementia with Lewy bodies
2. Parkinson's disease dementia

LBD usually begins around 50 years of age. It appears to affect more men than women.

The disease lasts an average of five to seven years from the time of diagnosis; however, it can be a shorter duration or last longer.

Lewy bodies are known to affect different areas of the brain. Parts of the brain affected are areas which control:

- Processing of information
- Perception
- Thought process
- Language
- Emotion
- Behavior
- Movement

- Sleep
- Alertness
- Smell

Dementia with Lewy bodies is characterized by cognitive symptoms appearing within a year of the onset of motion and movement difficulties.

Symptoms which are recognizable with dementia with Lewy bodies include:

- Hallucinations early in the course of the dementia
- Fluctuations in cognitive ability, attention, and alertness
- Rigidity, difficulty walking, and slowness
- Sensitivity to medication used for hallucination

Parkinson's disease dementia is also characterized by disabling cognitive symptoms developing more than a year after motion and movement difficulties start.

Recognizable symptoms with Parkinson's disease dementia are:

- Slow movements
- Muscle stiffness / tremors
- Shuffling walk

These symptoms usually result in a diagnosis of Parkinson's disease. Over time, as disabling cognitive symptoms develop, the diagnosis will be expanded to Parkinson's disease dementia.

It is important to note that not all people diagnosed with Parkinson's disease develop dementia.

With Parkinson's disease dementia, memory loss and disorientation do not occur first. More often, your loved one will experience greater problems with things like planning, decision-making, and organization.

They may also experience difficulties with visual perception, such as judging and navigating distances. This can cause them to fall frequently or become lost in familiar settings.

Behavior and Mood Problems

Behavior and mood changes can occur for several reasons, including:

Hallucinations

These are sensory experiences that cannot be verified by anyone other than the person experiencing them.

An example of this: Your loved one may be sitting in a recliner and suddenly start yelling at the kids running and screaming through the house—when the kids are not really there, or your loved one may see bugs crawling on the wall—when there are no bugs.

Delusions

These are beliefs that are contrary to the fact. An example of this is your loved one may look at you and say, "You are not my wife."

Stress, Anxiety, Fears

Your loved one may experience feelings of anxiety related to certain fears that may become magnified. For example, a fear of an electrical fire may cause your loved one to unplug or even cut all plugs from all electrical appliances, or they may insist on turning off all of the lights for fear that the light will malfunction and cause a fire.

Pain

Your loved one may become easily agitated if they are unable to do something they would normally enjoy due to pain. For instance, they enjoy baking, but they cannot even get started with a recipe because bending to lift metal pans from the cabinets has become an impossible task due to arthritis pain. They may become extremely agitated, angry, and resentful as a result.

Illness

Your loved one may not be able to tell you they are not feeling well. For instance, they may be experiencing cold symptoms and not realize that their nose is running, and they may be resistant or even angry to any kind of assistance when they are offered tissues.

Medications

Your loved one may refuse to take medication, or they may pocket the medication in their cheek and spit it out after you leave.

*NOTE: First and foremost, if your loved one's behavior or mood has changed and they exhibit any of the above or other new changes, seek the advice of your loved one's physician. Once you have ruled out physical illness, pain or underlying medical condition or reaction to medications, you can look at other causes.

Shared Motor and Cognitive Symptoms

Obtaining a diagnosis of LBD can be difficult in the initial stage because it has characteristics and symptoms similar to Parkinson's disease and Alzheimer's disease.

Parkinson's Disease and LBD— Shared Motor Symptoms

Tremor

The tremor, a shaking or trembling movement, usually appears when your loved one's muscles are at rest or relaxed, thus the term "resting tremor." A finger or other affected body part trembles when it is not performing an action. The tremor usually stops when a person begins an action.

Muscle Stiffness / Rigidity

Muscles normally stretch when they move and then relax when they are at rest. Rigidity means the muscle of your loved one's affected limb is always stiff and does not relax. This can contribute to a decreased range of motion. This can be uncomfortable or even painful.

Here are some examples of the challenges your loved one might experience in their ability to be active or engage in activities as a result of their stiff or rigid muscles:

- Getting in and out of the car for an outing to the store, a doctor's appointment, or a trip to the park.

- Enjoying activities such as dancing, taking a walk, turning their head to see an event or speak with someone who is not facing them directly.

- Getting in or out of a chair or bed.

Balance Difficulty / Postural Instability

Problems with balance or postural instability is another important shared symptom. Postural instability means your loved one may have a tendency to be unstable when standing upright. Postural instability occurs when your loved one has lost some of the reflexes needed for maintaining an upright posture. They might also have difficulty making turns or quick movements or even fall backwards.

Examples of activities that might be challenging because of these issues are:

- Getting up from a chair unassisted in order to move from one room to another.

- Taking a walk.

- Standing for pictures with family or friends.

- Dancing with a loved one.

- Outdoor activities such as gardening.

Gait Difficulties / Freezing

Gait is defined as a person's manner of walking, stepping, or running. People who experience freezing will normally hesitate before stepping forward. They feel like their feet are glued to the floor. Freezing is often temporary, and a person can enter a normal stride once he or she gets past the first step.

Freezing often occurs in very specific situations, such as when a person is starting to walk, pivoting, crossing a threshold or doorway, and when approaching a chair.

Various types of cues, such as an exaggerated first step, can help with freezing. Some individuals have severe freezing, in which they simply cannot take a step. Freezing is a potentially serious problem, as it may increase a person's risk of falling forward.

Slow Movement (Bradykinesia)

Slow movement or bradykinesia describes a general reduction of spontaneous movement.

It can give the appearance of stillness or make it difficult to perform repetitive movements. It can also cause a decrease in facial expressivity, which means your loved one may look like they have a blank stare. This can make it difficult to read your loved one's facial expressions which we will address later in this book.

With bradykinesia, your loved one may walk with short, shuffling steps. Your loved one with both rigidity and bradykinesia might not swing their arms when walking.

In addition, your loved one's speech may be affected. It may become quieter and less distinct as the disease progresses due to the reduction and limited range of movement caused by bradykinesia.

Some challenges your loved one might experience in their ability to be active or engage in activities as a result of slow movement or bradykinesia include:

- Activities of daily living such as buttoning a shirt, cutting food, or brushing teeth.

- Having a conversation or answering questions in a timeframe that meets someone else's expectation of the appropriate length of time.

  *NOTE: As the caregiver, you must ensure that others give your loved one time to speak.

- Repetitive movements such as writing, tapping a finger, moving a foot to the rhythm of music, or dialing a phone number.

Alzheimer's Disease and LBD— Shared Cognitive Symptoms

Communication Difficulties

With Lewy body dementia, your loved one might not be able to find the right words to tell you things such as having to go to the bathroom or what they would like to eat.

Behavioral Changes

As your loved one's cognitive abilities decrease, you may see some of the following behavioral issues even though your loved one would never have done any of these prior to the disease onset and progression:

- Taking things that do not belong to them.

- Making inappropriate sexual comments.

- Demanding and making unreasonable requests.

- Not complying with "normal" social conduct, such as talking loudly in church.

- Saying things that we might think but would never say to someone.

Poor Judgment

Similar to a rise in behavioral challenges, you may notice a rise in poor judgment or bad decisions as the disease progresses. Chances are you would have never thought this possible from your loved one prior to the onset or progression of LBD. Some examples include:

- Making choices that put their safety at risk, such as being out in the cold without a jacket.

- Inability to distinguish the important from the unimportant.

- Misjudging the intentions of others.

- Giving away large sums of money.

- Neglecting personal care and safety.

Confusion

Lewy body dementia can cause your loved one to be confused. Engaging in activities or actions that they once did without giving a second thought might be dangerous, such as:

- Trying to grab a hot pan that has been on the stove all day, or trying to get out of a moving car.

- Trying to walk in the house from a carpeted area to a tile area, and they think they have to step down or step up.

- A black welcome mat could appear as a hole, and your loved one may try to step over it or walk around it.

Chapter 2

Personal Care, Activities, and Help You Bring In

Lewy body dementia may or may not affect your loved one's personality, but it will affect their ability to interpret and deal with their surroundings as they did in the past.

"Activities" and "Activities of Daily Living" (ADLs) are critical parts of caring for a loved one at home. They require knowledge of your loved one's habits, preferences, abilities, and routines. This is the foundation for engaging your loved one. Caregivers also need to have the ability to communicate with your loved one and execute a planned activity.

All activities should be planned to offer the best opportunity to enhance your loved one's sense of well-being and reduce your stress. However, "life happens," and unplanned events, big or small, can disrupt the day, the week, or the month. Having the flexibility to adjust to what is happening with your loved one is vital.

An example of "life happens": You are caring for your loved one and have made sacrifices to be able to meet their needs. Most days you do not have help, and you enjoy the daily peace when your loved one takes a nap. One day, you put your loved one to bed for a nap after what had been a very long and tiring morning. You have been feeling isolated and alone for quite a while and decide to sit down with a well-deserved cup of tea and connect with a friend over the phone. During the course of the conversation with your friend, your loved one wakes up and decides to go to the bathroom. She does not make it in time. She is upset and agitated, and you hang up on your friend to run to the bathroom. You are not quite sure what to do to calm your loved one as you try to help clean her. You finally get her settled down, but she is now refusing to go back to bed. Your loved one's normal two-hour nap where you get a few minutes to yourself and can quietly do whatever you want for yourself is gone. You now need to figure something out to keep your loved one engaged for the rest of the day.

Activities should promote or enhance your loved one's physical, cognitive, and emotional health. In this book, we will focus on leisure activities and the activities of daily living with common sense approaches. We will offer suggestions and tips on the "How To's" of getting your loved one engaged, dressed, and fed.

Our goals with this book are to:

- Provide family caregivers with the knowledge and tools to allow them to engage their loved one so that both can enjoy the benefits of activities.

- Offer a starting point that will provide continuity of approach regarding care, communication, and information-gathering to minimize changes and acclimation time if your loved one does have to move from home to an institutional setting.

Our goal is to help you deliver meaningful programs of interest to your loved one that focus on physical, social, spiritual, cognitive, and recreational activities. Everyone involved in the care for your loved one should be "on the same page" to minimize changes and challenges that your loved one will face.

The importance of understanding your family dynamics and the importance of each role ANY individual plays in the care for your loved one is critical. As the dementia progresses, roles will evolve, and everyone needs to understand that this is a process.

Being a primary caregiver is a 24/7 job. Without help, you are always on call and run the risk of becoming physically and mentally exhausted. If you choose to use the services of a home care agency while caring for your loved one at home, please ask if they have a Home Care Certified professional on staff and make sure that the caregiver you choose has received basic training on Leisure Activities and Activities of Daily Living. This will assist with continuity of approach, communication, and planning that will benefit both you and your loved one.

When you do bring in help, make sure all of your loved one's caregivers (full-time, part-time, family and friends) use the same approach for activities and interaction that you do. With a common approach, there are significantly less opportunities to disrupt routines and make unsettling changes that affect you and your loved one long after the help has left.

A common approach is key. Demand it!

The Four Pillars of Activities

There are four areas that you should focus on for engaging your loved one in any type of activity. We call them the Four Pillars of Activities.

First Pillar of Activities: Know your Loved One—Information Gathering and Assessment

- Have a Personal History Form completed.

- Know them—who they are, who they were, and what their functional abilities are today.

- Make sure all caregivers know this information as well.

Second Pillar of Activities: Communicating and Motivating for Success

- Communication is key. Each caregiver must know how to effectively communicate with your loved one and be consistent with techniques.

Third Pillar of Activities: Customary Routines and Preferences

- As best as possible, maintain a routine and daily plan based on your loved one's needs and preferences.

Fourth Pillar of Activities: Planning and Executing Activities

- Based on all of the information you have gathered about your loved one, you have the opportunity to offer engaging activities that are appropriate and meet your loved one's personal preferences.

The Benefits of Activities with a Standard Approach

Caregiver Benefits of Standard Approach to Activities

Planned and well-executed activities result in less stress for the caregiver as well as less stress for your loved one. Whether the activity involves playing a game or bathing, a standard approach where as many details as possible are pre-planned can make a significant, positive difference for everyone. Knowing what to expect, to the best one can, helps empower all involved and enable a level of control when so much has changed.

Social Benefits of Activities

Activities offer the opportunity for increased social interaction between family members, friends, caregivers, and the one being cared for. Activities create positive experiences and memories for everyone. When possible, consider accessing community-based programs for additional support.

Behavioral Benefits of Activities

Well-planned and well-executed activities of any type can reduce challenging behaviors that sometimes arise when caring for someone with dementia.

Self-Esteem Benefits of Activities

Leisure activities offered with just the right level of challenge provide your loved one with an opportunity for success. This is also true with personal care routines such as dressing. Success during activities improves your loved one's sense of self-esteem.

Sleep Benefits of Activities

As part of a daily routine, activities can improve sleeping at night. If a loved one is inactive all day, it is likely that person will nap periodically. Napping can interrupt good sleep patterns at night.

Chapter 3

First Pillar of Activities: Know Your Loved One— Information Gathering and Assessment

Get to know your loved one again. Not just who they are today, but who they were their whole life. This is the foundation of engaging your loved one. Knowing your loved one is the First Pillar of Activities.

Details matter. Gather as much information as you can for yourself and all caregivers who may help with your loved one.

Basic knowledge is essential. The little things are important.

What activities did they enjoy doing?

What is your loved one capable of doing: physically, cognitively?

Do their abilities fluctuate from day to day? These abilities may vary greatly from what they could do prior to the onset of Lewy body dementia and may change often in the future.

Caregivers

Figure out who your loved one is the most comfortable with when needing care.

Do they prefer a female/male, or specific caregiver?

Sex and age of the caregiver can be a significant issue.

Illnesses and Limitations

What other physical illness or limitations does your loved one have? These are just as important to know as the personal history information so that all caregivers can provide the highest level of care.

As the primary caregiver, you may already know most of the answers to the items listed next, but recording them in a Personal History Form (at the end of this book) is a good and necessary exercise to be completed by you, other family members, and other caregivers. Everyone has different memories and information about your loved one. When you put all of that information together, you paint a complete picture.

You might have heard offers from many people to help. The first thing they can do is share their memories of your loved one with you or fill out a Personal History Form as completely as possible.

At minimum, gather the following information as best as you can:

Basic Information

- Name, preferred name to be called, age, and date of birth

Background Information

- Place of birth, cultural/ethnic background, marital status, children (how many and their names), religion/church, military service/employment, education level, and primary language spoken

Medical and Dietary/Nutritional Information

- Any formal diagnosis, allergies, and food regimen/diets

Habits

- Drinking/alcohol, smoking, exercise, and other daily habits

Physical Status

- Abilities/limitations, visual aids, hearing deficits, speech, communication, hand dominance, and mobility/gait

Mental Status

- Alertness; cognitive abilities/limitations; orientation to family, time, place, person, routine; ability to follow directions; preference for written or verbal instructions; ability to comprehend and follow one-step versus multi-step directions; safety awareness; safety concerns; etc.

Social Status

- One-on-one interaction; communication with others through written words, phone calls, or other means such as email, Twitter, or Facebook

Emotional Status

- Level of contentment, outgoing/withdrawn, extroverted/introverted, dependent/independent, easily frustrated, easygoing

Leisure Status

- Past, present, and possible future interests

- Enjoys solitary versus social activities

- Physical versus passive (playing a sport versus watching a movie)

You can use the R.O.S. Personal History form to gather additional information from friends, family, and yourself. No matter how you gather the information, there are two important items that you should take note of.

First, any form that is used to gather personal history should be a living document. It needs constant updating as the dementia and physical changes progress. It is also important to remember that with dementia, what works today won't work tomorrow, and may not work five minutes from now!

Second, you and your loved one may have been very private people. Having dementia will change that. Gathering information and sharing with other caregivers is critical. Your loved one's past pleasures, likes and activities will become the cornerstones of the communication process for everyone.

There may be something in your loved one's past that happened years ago that you might consider embarrassing or private. If you choose not to share, please understand that one way or another, it very likely will come out.

Caregivers and family members that offer assistance are not there to judge you or your loved one on something that happened years or even decades ago. They are there to help you in your moment of need today. Information is vital, and being armed with good information allows all caregivers the opportunity to turn a "bad" day into a "good" day through proper communication.

Informal Assessments

Informal assessments are done through interviews, observations, and information gathered through other means. These will allow you and others to "fill in the blanks" of the R.O.S. Personal History Form.

Interviews

Interviews are conducted with your loved one, or with family members, friends, or significant others.

Observations

Observations are what you and others have seen or heard concerning your loved one, e.g., how they interact with others, their behavior, and their responses to questions or statements made by others. This includes body language and expressions. You have probably seen these interactions a thousand times and made a mental note whenever something stuck out. Now, you must write them down for your future use and for others.

During their assessments, four people might all say they like "cooking," yet they might not actually have the same specific activity in mind—or even enjoy the same activity.

- Person 1—Enjoys preparing a full Southern-style meal for their family every Sunday. Everyone would get together after church. The day was spent in and around the kitchen with everyone involved in preparing the meal and socializing, from the women kneading the dough for the bread, to the children shucking the green beans, to the men barbequing the meat outside. Much laughter and love was shared.

- Person 2—Enjoys baking all sorts of desserts from scratch with their children.

- Person 3—Enjoys a quick meal, already prepared. Just warms it up and it's ready to serve for an informal get-together with some friends.

- Person 4—Enjoys grilling anything from vegetables to hot dogs. Does not like cooking indoors.

As you can see from these examples, details matter. Gather as much information as you can for yourself and all caregivers who may help with your loved one.

The R.O.S. Personal History Form at the back of this book is a great tool for you to use to provide all caregivers the basic information of your loved one's interests and past. You may download a copy of the Personal History Form at www.StartSomeJoy.org.

Functional Levels

In addition to the information gathered in the Personal History Form—which tells everyone what your loved one enjoys, who that person is, and what his or her personal preferences might be—we also need to look at your loved one's functional level. This will allow you to plan activities that your loved one can accomplish. There are many functional scales available, but for our purpose, we will use the four levels as follow.

Level 1

Your loved one has good social skills. They are able to communicate. They are alert and oriented to person, place and time, and they have a long attention span.

Level 2

Your loved one has less social skills, and their verbal skills may be impaired as well. They may have some behavior symptoms. They may need something to do, and may have an increased energy level, but they have a shorter attention span.

Level 3

Your loved one has less social skills. Their verbal skills are even more impaired than they were at Level 2. They are also easily distracted. They may have some visual/spatial perception and balance concerns, and they need maximum assistance with their care.

Level 4

Your loved one has a low energy level, nonverbal communication skills, and they rarely initiate contact with others, however, they may respond if given time and cues.

With the personal history and functional level information, you and every caregiver have the greatest opportunity to provide person-appropriate activities for your loved one.

Chapter 4

Second Pillar of Activities: Communicating and Motivating for Success

Successful communication and recognizing your loved one's ability to understand what is being said is critical to your success in caregiving. This is the Second Pillar of Activities.

The key to effective communication is the *ability to listen* attentively. That means listening with your ears and your eyes using the knowledge of your loved one's history and habits. This includes you listening to your loved one and your loved one listening to you.

For example, asking your loved one a question about something as simple as if they would like a sandwich for lunch can set the stage for a challenging mealtime.

Why? Because your loved one may not understand what is being said to them. Just because they shake their head yes or no, that does not always mean your loved one understands or even hears what you or another caregiver may be saying. Your loved one may not want to admit they have not understood or heard you.

Make sure that the message you are trying to convey, no matter what it is, is heard by your loved one. This requires all caregivers to use communication techniques that provide an open, nonthreatening environment for your loved one.

Listening behavior can either enhance and encourage or shut down communication altogether. You need to assess your listening style and be able to assess the listening styles of the other caregivers and family members working with your loved one.

Verbal Communication

Communication is simply an interactive process whereby information is exchanged. More importantly, though, communication is a way to connect with another person. How well you connect depends on your ability to respond appropriately and give feedback on something that was communicated. It also depends on your ability to *listen*.

Verbal Communication Tips

- Use exact, short, positive phrases. Repeat twice if necessary. Have your loved one repeat back what was said.

- Speak slowly with words your loved one knows.

- Allow time for your loved one to answer.

- Give one instruction at a time. Provide only the number of steps your loved one can handle at a time.

- Use a friendly, respectful tone of voice.

- If your loved one has a visual impairment, be sure to use verbal cues to let him or her know you are engaged.

- Talk to your loved one like an adult.

Nonverbal Communication

Although it may seem that most communication happens verbally, research has shown that actually most communication occurs nonverbally. Facial expressions, eye contact, gestures, and even the amount of physical space between you and your loved one are nonverbal ways to communicate. Nonverbal communication can go a long way to convey your message and make your connection stronger, but it can also undercut your attempts to communicate if your nonverbal cues contradict your intention or send mixed signals.

The key elements to consider regarding how you communicate nonverbally include:

Facial Expressions

- Be aware of what your facial expressions are conveying to your loved one. Your mood will be mirrored.

- Be careful if you're tired or stressed that your face doesn't show a bad mood. If your loved one asks, "What's wrong?" he or she may be reading a tense look on your face. Taking a few deep breaths can help you relax your facial expression.

Eye Contact

- Ensure that you have made eye contact with your loved one and that his or her attention is focused on you and what you are saying.

- It might be difficult for your loved one to understand what you're saying without seeing your face and eyes.

Gestures and Touch

- Calmly use nonverbal signs such as pointing, waving, and other hand gestures in combination with what you are saying.

- If your loved one misunderstands some words, visual cues and gestures can help them keep up with the conversation or understand what you'd like done.

Tone of Voice

- The inflection in your voice helps your loved one relate to the words you are saying.

- Words convey facts, but the *feeling* in every interaction is in the tone. You know the difference in a friendly, respectful response and a frustrated or rushed answer. The difference is often not in *what* someone says, but rather *how* it is said. Keeping your tone calm, friendly, and respectful—the way we talk to adults—can help your loved one feel better about your communication.

Body Language

- Be aware of the position of your hands and arms when talking to your loved one.

- Similar to the tone of your voice, your body language sends a message, usually about your mood or feelings. For example, if your arms are crossed, it might send the message that you're upset or closed to an idea. If your head is propped in your hands, it might look like you're tired or bored. Pay attention to your loved one's body language too. You may be able to see a change in mood by watching body language. Adjust your support to make him or her more comfortable.

General Nonverbal Communication Tips

- Always approach your loved one from the front before addressing.

- Place yourself at eye level with the person to whom you are talking.

- Don't touch unexpectedly; it might startle your loved one.

- Give nonverbal praises such as smiles and head nods.

- Be an active listener.

Being a Detective

As your loved one's dementia progresses, there will be many days that you will not know what kind of day it will be until after it has started. If there is an issue, the starting point in your process is communicating to figure out what they are telling you.

Imagine that one day you find your loved one in the living room having just left the kitchen with a cup of "coffee" in an unsteady hand. You ask, "What do you have there?"

Your loved one proudly says with a smile, "I made coffee!" You take one look at the cup and see that it is a dark-colored liquid full of what seem to be coffee grounds, but you are not sure. It is now time to play detective as you quickly inspect the cup to figure out what it really is. You tell your loved one that you will dry the cup off and get some paper napkins from the kitchen. To your surprise, the coffeemaker is still intact and full of the coffee you had just made. So what did your loved one make? You open the cabinet next to the coffee to find that all of the tea bags had been torn open and poured into the sugar container and that was what the "grounds" in the cup were. You are thankful it was not anything else and throw the "coffee" out.

After you clean everything up, you get a fresh cup of real coffee to give to your loved one in the living room where he is waiting, and you proceed to tell him how great the coffee was that he made and that you will have a cup, too. The afternoon ends on a pleasant note with the two of you sharing a cup of coffee and conversation. If you had chided your loved one as soon as you saw the "coffee" he made earlier, things could have easily turned into a negative experience for the both of you.

Validation

In 1963, Naomi Feil, the developer of the Validation Therapy techniques, began working with people over the age of 80 who were disoriented. Her initial goals were to help these people face reality and relate to each other in a group. In 1966, she concluded that helping them face reality was unrealistic. Each person was trapped in a world of fantasy. Exploring feelings and reminiscing encouraged group members to respond better to each other. Music stimulated group cohesion and feelings of well-being. Mrs. Feil said, "I abandoned the goal of reality orientation when I found group members withdrew, or became increasingly hostile, whenever I tried to orient them to an intolerable present reality."

To validate is to acknowledge the feelings of a person. To validate is to say that their feelings are true. Denying feelings invalidates the individual. Validation uses empathy to tune in to the inner reality of disoriented loved ones. Empathy, or walking in the shoes of the other, builds trust. Trust brings safety. Safety brings strength. Strength renews feelings of worth. Worth reduces stress. With empathy, the caregiver picks up their clues and helps put their loved one's feelings into words. This validates their loved one and restores their dignity.

The goals of validation are:

- Restore self-worth
- Reduce stress
- Justify living
- Work toward resolving unfinished conflicts from the past
- Reduce the need for chemical and physical restraints

- Increase verbal and nonverbal communication

- Prevent withdrawal inward to vegetation

Mrs. Feil is a pioneer and R.O.S. encourages every caregiver to use validation instead of reality orientation. Here is an example:

Your loved one is looking for her "baby." You know that she enjoys holding a stuffed cat which she wraps up in a blanket. She will sometimes say how much work it is to care for and how hard it can be. She will "feed" this stuffed animal and will happily share that the "baby" is "eating" and growing well. She will often sing it to sleep.

After several feedings you could no longer wipe the stuffed animal off. You had to wash the "baby" in the washing machine, and it is now spinning around in the dryer.

This needs to be done quickly before your loved one realizes the baby is gone and becomes upset.

Too late—you should have timed this better.

Now you must make up a story about where the "baby" is and hope your loved one believes you.

In the past, you have tried other "babies" which only ended in cursing and screaming from your loved one.

For whatever reason, this "baby" is special to her, and so you go on to tell her that the "baby" is sleeping, and you don't want to disturb her. You suggest, "Let's make something in the kitchen for her to eat when she wakes up." Your loved one agrees, and as you finish making sandwiches with your loved one, you breathe a sigh of relief when you hear the buzzer from the dryer go off.

*NOTE: Please be aware that other family members or maybe even you might have a problem with validation. Let us use the example above. You and your wife have been married many years. You think it is ridiculous that she would walk around with a stuffed animal and call it a "baby." You scold her each time she does and take the stuffed animal away because you think it is beneath her, and it is embarrassing for you. When you take the stuffed animal away, this causes crying, anger and angst. If that is what you choose to do, then so be it. But consider this question: Would you rather have crying, anger and angst or happiness with a stuffed animal or baby doll. As the primary caregiver, it is your choice.

Approaches to Successful Communication and Activities

There are simple strategies to communicate with your loved one now that the basics of verbal, nonverbal, and validation have been covered. No matter how tired you are, or how upset you may be with your situation, please remember to:

Be Calm

Always approach your loved one in a relaxed and calm demeanor. Your mood will be mirrored by your loved one. Smiles are contagious.

Be Flexible

There is no right or wrong way to complete a task. Offer praise and encouragement for the efforts your loved one has put into a task. If you notice your loved one becoming overwhelmed or frustrated, stop the task, and re-approach at another time. Likewise, if you feel yourself getting overwhelmed or

frustrated, take a time-out, take some deep
breaths, and approach it again when you're
feeling in control.

Be Nonresistive

Don't force tasks on your loved one. Adults do
not want to be told, "No!" or directed on what
to do. The power of suggestion goes a long
way, and you get more with an ounce of sugar
than a pound of vinegar.

Be Guiding, but Not Controlling

Always use a soft, gentle approach, and mind
your p's, q's, and tone of voice. Your facial
expressions must match the words you are
saying. If something is not working, back off,
change something about your communication,
the task, or the environment, and try again.
Because communication may become difficult
with Lewy body dementia, recognizing your
loved one's ability to understand what is being
said is significant to your success in caregiving.

Barriers to Good Communication

There are generally two barriers that negatively affect communication with your loved one—Caregiver and Environmental. Here are some tips on how to eliminate negative barriers.

Caregiver Barriers

- Slow down when speaking. Use a calm tone of voice, but not a childish tone, and be aware of your hand movements.

- Never be demanding or commanding.

- Never argue with a person with impaired cognition. You will never win the argument.

- Enter their world. Live their truth.

- Do not offer long explanations when answering questions.

Environmental Barriers

- Minimize noise from air conditioners and home appliances. Turn off appliances and move directly in front of your loved one so you do not have to shout across a room to compete with the air conditioner.

- If the TV is on in the same room where you are trying to talk, turn the volume down.

- If a window is open and there is outside traffic and noise, close the window, and move directly in front of your loved one.

- Check your loved one's hearing aid battery, and make sure that it is not whistling. Please check to make sure that your loved one's hearing aids are working properly on a regular basis.

- Adjust the lighting in the room. If the lighting in a room negatively affects your loved one's vision, they may be more focused on trying to see rather than on communicating with you.

Communication and Behavior

Behaviors are a means to communicate when words are no longer effective.

Caregivers must uncover the meaning behind the behaviors and put a plan into effect to manage those needs. Remember, be a detective.

Aggressive Behaviors

Aggressive behaviors can include hitting, angry outbursts, obscenities, yelling, racial insults, making inappropriate sexual comments, and/or biting. Trying to communicate with or provide care to a person who is aggressive can be stressful and even frightening for caregivers.

Possible Causes for Aggression

- Too much noise or overstimulation—the television might be on, the dogs might be barking, and you might be yelling to them

from the kitchen to see if they are ready
for lunch.

- Cluttered environment—the house or
the room your loved one is in might be
a mess.

- Uncomfortable room temperatures—too
hot or too cold.

- Your loved one's basic needs not being
met—hunger, thirst, needing to use the
bathroom, needing comfort.

- Pain of any type—headache, sore bottom
from rash, diabetic nerve pain.

- Fear, anxiety or confusion—your loved
one may become afraid and confused
because they may not recognize you, or
they may mistake you for someone else.

Another example of something that
happens often is: Your loved one moved in
with you two years ago when their health
became a concern. They left the only
house they had ever lived in during their
adult life. Their dementia is causing them

to believe that they are 30 years younger and still live at their old home, and they want to go home.

- Communication barriers—we discussed barriers earlier, but your loved one may also only be able to engage in limited conversation because they are unable to find the words they need to express themselves.

- Caregiver's mood—they can read you and all caregivers like a book. If you are having a bad day, leave it in the other room or at the door before you walk in to interact with your loved one.

- Feeling that they are being rushed—it might take extra time to absorb and understand what you or another caregiver consider simple directions.

- Difficulty seeing activity or materials of activity, which prevents them from participating.

- Lack of independence—may lead to a feeling of worthlessness as your loved one relies heavily upon you and other caregivers.

Interventions to Mitigate Aggressive Behaviors

- Identify the triggers of the aggression. Be a detective. There is never a behavior that *just occurs*. Try reminiscing with your loved one about specific details of their past to divert attention until you can identify the cause. This is why knowledge of your loved one and who they were is so important.

- Communicate for success. Use the skills you have learned in this book. Be guiding, but not controlling.

- Validate and support their feelings.

- Remain calm, and speak in a soft tone.

- Find items that they find comfort in, e.g., a picture of the family.

- Provide consistent caregivers and schedules. Stick to your loved one's routine.

- Engage in recreational activities that match their abilities and interests, as tolerated.

- When giving instructions, don't overwhelm your loved one. Break down instructions into one-step increments. If needed, demonstrate what is required with hand-over-hand assistance and offer praise and gentle encouragement.

- Keep an ongoing dialogue between family members and caregivers over any noted changes in patterns or behaviors.

- Help your loved one to slow down and relax.

- Play or listen to music your loved one enjoys for its calming effects.

- Use spiritual support if this is important to your loved one.

Chapter 5

Third Pillar of Activities: Customary Routines and Preferences

Maintaining your loved one's customary routines, and basing activities on your loved one's preferences is the Third Pillar of Activities.

For the purpose of developing a daily plan of care, we will be discussing two areas: Daily Customary Routine and Activity Preferences. The goal is to gain from your loved one's perspective how important certain aspects of care/activity are of interest to them as an individual.

Daily Customary Routine

Your loved one has distinct lifestyle preferences and routines that should be preserved to the greatest extent possible. All reasonable accommodation should be made to maintain your loved one's lifestyle preferences.

Always understand, know, and remember that longtime preferences may change as a result of the Lewy body dementia.

Be prepared for such changes so you can continue to accommodate your loved one's preferences as much as possible. When a person feels like their control has been removed and preferences are being disregarded and not respected as an individual, it can be demoralizing.

Activity Preferences

Activities are a way for individuals to establish meaning in their lives.

A lack of opportunity to engage in meaningful and enjoyable activities can result in boredom, depression, and behavioral disturbances.

Here is an activity suggestion that can be helpful. It is always good when the caregiver utilizes whatever is around the house.

Card Games

Card games are some of the easier games to play, and adjusting the rules as necessary to ensure a positive outcome and foster your loved one's self-esteem is okay.

*NOTE: Many groups will make the blanket suggestion to "play cards" as a way to engage your loved one. We agree with that, but encourage you to take it a step further to be successful. You must identify your loved one's card game preference as well as their cognitive and physical strengths and weaknesses. Once those have been identified, you can adjust the game and play accordingly. Set your loved one up for success, not failure.

- Play Go Fish with a standard deck of cards.

- Play memory matching with pictures of family members by printing pictures and turning them into cards.

- The card game Uno can be used in many ways. Some examples are:

  - Play the game as intended
  - Utilize the Uno cards for color matching or number matching.
  - You do not have to play a game at all— just let your loved one hold the playing cards in their hands for the tactile stimulation.

Individuals vary in the activities they prefer, reflecting unique personalities, past interest, perceived environmental constraints, religious and cultural background, and changing physical and mental abilities. We as family caregivers have a great opportunity to empower a loved one to see that they still possess many great talents and abilities. By modifying or adapting an activity to allow them to engage at an independent level, you are restoring their self-esteem and self-worth.

Chapter 6

Fourth Pillar of Activities:
Planning and Executing Activities

Planning and executing activities is the Fourth Pillar of Activities. With the knowledge of your loved one's history, functional level, effective communication techniques to use, and their daily routine, we now look at planning activities at which they can be successful.

The Lesson Plan

A *lesson plan* is a tool that you can use to help plan activities for your loved one. A good lesson plan consists of a list of items needed to complete the activity, clear instructions, and room to record any and all observations regarding your loved one's participation and engagement.

As your loved one's abilities and responses change, those changes will dictate how you modify an activity to meet their current needs and abilities. The lesson plan is an ever-changing document. It is meant to be written on to note the changes you made to the original plan, so that the family member or caregiver working with your loved one next can follow your modifications in the hopes of recreating a positive experience.

Items in the Lesson Plan

Date

Document the date the program is used with your loved one.

Program Name

You can rename the program if you or your loved one prefer.

Objective of Activity

Our goal is to provide meaningful activities. People have a need to be productive, and they want to engage in something with a purpose. List the objectives of the program.

Materials

List suggested materials to use with this program.

Prerequisite Skills

Detail the skills your loved one needs to participate in this program.

Activity Outline

Include step-by-step instructions to complete this program.

Evaluation

When you or a family member are conducting an activity with your loved one, documenting results and responses is critical to identifying ways to improve activity programs for your loved one. Items to document should include:

- <u>Verbal cues, physical assistance, or modifications you required for this activity.</u> What strategies seemed to work best? Which ones did not work so well?

- <u>How your loved one responded to this program</u>. Did this increase frustration levels or seem to calm the individual?

- <u>Whether your loved one enjoyed this activity</u>. What did he or she like or dislike about the activity?

- <u>Pay attention to other factors that might have affected the outcome</u>— distractions like phone calls, time of day, weather, etc.

A blank template is included on the next page to give you an example of what a lesson plan looks like.

*NOTE: Make sure caregivers and family members are consistent with the type of verbal cues, physical assistance, or modifications that produce positive results.

Lesson Plan Template

Date	Program Name

Objective of Activity

Materials

Prerequisite Skills

Activity Outline

Evaluation

Chapter 7

Leisure Activity Categories, Types, Topics, and Tips

Activity Categories

Now that we have gone through the Four Pillars of Activities, let's look at various leisure activities. Activities are generally broken down into three different categories: Maintenance Activities, Supportive Activities, and Empowering Activities.

Maintenance Activities

Maintenance activities are traditional activities that help your loved one to maintain physical, cognitive, social, spiritual, and emotional health. Examples include:

- Using manipulative games such as those in the R.O.S. Legacy System
- Craft and art activities

- Attending church services
- Working crossword and trivia puzzles like the *How Much Do You Know About* puzzles found at www.TheROSStore.com
- Taking a walk
- Tai chi

Supportive Activities

Supportive activities are for those that have a lower tolerance for traditional activities. These types of activities provide a comfortable environment while providing stimulation or solace. Examples include:

- Listening to and singing music
- Hand massages
- Relaxation activities
  - Aromatherapy
  - Meditation
  - Bird-watching

<u>**Empowering Activities**</u>

Empowering activities help your loved one build and maintain self-respect by offering opportunities for self-expression and responsibility. Examples include:

- Cooking
- Making memory boxes
- Folding laundry

Activity Types

Once you have chosen an activity from a category that will suit your loved one's need, you must choose an activity type that will interest them. There are several types of activities to choose from. Below are some examples:

<u>**Art Activities**</u>

- Coloring—Using a template

- Painting—Using a template or creating an original

- Dancing—Any form your loved one wants

- Creating collages using tissue paper and paste

- Creating murals using magazine cutouts and paste

- Drawing still life images such as a vase of flowers or a suspension bridge

Craft Activities

- Jewelry making

- Knitting

- Scrapbooking

- Card making

- Clay modeling

- Creating and decorating memory boxes

- Building model planes or cars

- Flower making with tissue paper

Verbal Activities

- Conversation
- Trivia
- Word games
- Sing-along/karaoke

Entertainment Activities

- Board games, card games
- Video games
- Crossword puzzles

Listening Activities

- Music
- Storytelling
- Books on tape
- Listening to the nostalgic radio programs available on the internet
- Listening to poetry or other inspirational readings
- Bible study on tape

Visual Activities

- Watching a movie
- Watching a performance
- Bird-watching
- People-watching from the front porch or in a local park

Writing Activities

- Writing a story or poem
- Writing a letter

Active Activities

- Dancing
- Folding laundry
- Road trips

Activity Topics

Once you know what type of activity you want to engage your loved one from, here are some suggestions for activity topics:

Colors

- Colors of their favorite sports team
- Colors of their wedding
- Colors of flowers or cars

Music

- Favorite music
- Music from when they were younger and dating
- Patriotic songs
- Holiday songs
- Favorite artists from the age they think they are, e.g., if they believe they are 25 years old, use popular singers or songs of that era

Military Service

- War stories
- World events of their time
- Their personal experiences of either military service or what it was like in the States

Holidays

- Specific holidays that coincide with their culture or religion
- Favorite holidays

Cooking

- Home cooking
- Comfort food
- Favorite recipes from their mother/grandmother
- Favorite food associated with events, holidays, family gatherings

Sports

- Professional sports teams they liked
- Their involvement in sports
- Big sporting events from their era

School Days

- Where they went to school
- Favorite school classes or teachers
- Memories of their children's school events

Old Cars

- Their family's first car
- Their first car
- Prices of cars now and then
- Dream cars

Places

- Where they were born
- Where they grew up
- Places they have been
- Vacations they took

Activity Tips for Individuals with Mild to Moderate Dementia

Many people have cognitive deficits that are significant enough to impact their day as well as their awareness of their surroundings. By providing activities that reinforce their past, we increase and improve their social skills which can improve their general interactions with others.

Validating Activities

Validating activities validate the memories and feelings of individuals who are considerably disoriented. They focus on the perception of what happened in the past.

Reminiscing Activities

Reminiscing activities are designed to help your loved one identify the important contributions he or she has made throughout their lifetime. It is an important part of human development to see oneself as a contributing member of society.

Resocializing Activities

Once your loved one can successfully participate in reminiscing and validating activities, it is time to encourage them, through resocializing activities, to build on those social skills and begin to expand their connections to the community in which they live. This can be as simple as interactions with a neighbor, in church, or within their community.

There is no magic pill for these areas, and one size does not fit all. Your loved one is unique, and there will be some trial and error as you work your way through validating, reminiscing, and resocializing activities using the Four Pillars of Activities.

Chapter 8

Activities of Daily Living
Tips and Suggestions

With Lewy body dementia, customary daily routines and preferences may change when least expected. The following pages contain tips and suggestions to help you and all caregivers with the basic activities of daily living.

Bathing

Bathing can be a relaxing, enjoyable experience—or a time of confrontation and anger. Use a calm approach. Your loved one's "usual" routine is very important.

Safety and Preparation

- Water temperature should range from 110-115 degrees Fahrenheit maximum to prevent burning or skin injury.

- Hot water can cause fatigue.

- The tub floor needs to be slip proof. Use a rubber mat that doesn't slide, or use permanent nonslip decals.

- Place a nonskid rug on the floor outside the tub to prevent slipping.

- Install grab bars. Always make sure the grab bars are properly and securely installed into the wall studs.

- Do not use bath oils.

Bathing—Know Your Loved One

- Is your loved one accustomed to a bath or shower?

- Can they get into a bath or shower without assistance?

- Can they soap their body or wash their hair alone?

- Can they independently dry with a towel, with simple tricks such as sewing straps onto towels to make them easier to hold?

- If they need help, who is your loved one the most comfortable with when needing assistance bathing?

Bathing—Communicating and Motivating

- Don't ask if they want to bathe. Simply say in an easy, friendly voice "Bath time."

- Use short, simple sentences.

- Look directly at your loved one.

- Always smile, and talk calmly and gently.

- Do not argue or try to explain "why."

Bathing—Customary Routines and Preferences

- What time of day does your loved one normally bathe?

- How often did your loved one bathe?

- What is the process that works for you and your loved one when it is time to bathe? Make sure all caregivers know each detail of the process. For example, is the water turned on and running prior to your loved one entering the tub? Is a towel placed on a shower chair for your loved one to use so the chill on their bottom is removed when they sit?

- Whatever the process, take it one step at a time, following their normal bathing routine. For example, your loved one may prefer that you wash their hair first and then their body, or they may prefer to soak for 10 minutes before washing.

- When assisting your loved one with bathing, have a towel ready to put over their shoulders or on their lap to minimize feelings of exposure.

- Be sure to have your loved one's favorite personal care products for familiar smell and feeling.

Bathing—Planning and Executing

- Have all care items and tools ready prior to starting the bath process.
  - A shower chair if necessary

- A handheld hose for showering and bathing

- A long-handled sponge or scrubbing brush if they would like to scrub themselves

- Sponges with soap inside or a soft soap applicator instead of bar soap (bar soap can easily slip out of your loved one's hand)

- Have a towel and clothing prepared for when the bath is finished.

- A second towel can be placed on the back of a chair to allow your loved one to dry their back by rubbing against the towel.

- Use a terry cloth robe instead of a towel to dry off.

Other Bathroom & Grooming Activities

Brushing Teeth

- If assistance is needed, start with step-by-step directions. This might not be as simple as you think. Take a moment and think of all of the steps necessary to brush your teeth, from walking into the bathroom, to finding the toothpaste in the drawer and removing the cap, to rinsing their mouth once they have finished brushing. Depending on your loved one's level of dementia, it might be easier to show them.

- For family members at home, brush your teeth at the same time.

- Use positive reinforcement, and compliment your loved one on the good job they are doing.

- Help your loved one to clean their dentures as needed.

Shaving

- Encourage a male to shave.

- Use an electric razor for safety.

- If they need assistance, please provide it.

- Give positive feedback, and avoid pointing out small mistakes.

Makeup

- If your loved one had been accustomed to wearing makeup, there is no reason for this to stop. If your loved one shows interest or a desire to wear makeup, encourage the familiar routine and offer assistance to apply if needed.

Hair

- Try to maintain hairstyle and care as your loved one did. However, if independence is more important, consider a style that allows independence. A shorter cut sometimes requires less work and finesse to maintain.

- Explain each step simply before you do anything to reduce any anxiety.

Nails

- Keep nails clean and trimmed. Be gentle while trimming your loved one's nails. Be mindful of how and where you place their fingers and arms.

- Offer to polish your loved one's nails.

- When polishing, engage your loved one in conversation.

- If your loved one had a normal/weekly schedule for nail care prior to the onset of Lewy body dementia, please try to maintain that schedule.

Toileting or Using the Bathroom

- Learn your loved one's individual habits and routines for using the toilet. This might not be something that you knew before and is part of the changing roles.

- Toilet routinely on rising, before and after meals, and at bedtime, at minimum.

- If your loved one is having trouble communicating, please watch for agitation, pulling at their clothes, or restlessness. This may be an indication that they need to go to the bathroom.

- Assist with clothing as needed, and be positive and pleasant while assisting.

- Provide verbal cues and instructions as needed. Be guiding, but not controlling.

Clothing

Clothing—Know Your Loved One

- Daily clothing choices should remain as they had been and based on your loved one's available wardrobe during the initial stages of the disease.

- As their dementia progresses, changes will have to be made. Clothes need to be comfortable and easy to remove, especially to go to bathroom.

- Choose clothes that are loose fitting and have elastic waistbands.

- For convenience, choose wraparound clothing instead of the pullover type.

- If possible, choose clothing that opens in the front, not the back. This prevents your loved one from having to reach behind the body and allows the feeling of independence from dressing oneself.

- When purchasing new clothes, look for clothing with large, flat buttons, Velcro closures, or zippers.

- To assist your loved one with zipping pants or a jacket, attach a zipper pull or leather loop on the end of the zipper.

- Have your loved one wear slip-on shoes if they will.

Clothing—Communicating and Motivating

- Use short, simple sentences, and provide instruction as needed.

- Always smile.

- Talk calmly and gently.
- Do not argue or try to explain "why."

Clothing—Routines and Preferences

- Enjoy a friendly discussion each evening about the next day's schedule and what your loved one may want to wear.

- Changes will have to be made as the LBD progresses. You may have to limit the choice of clothing, and leave only two outfits in their room at a time.

- If your loved one wants to wear the same thing every day, and if you can afford it, buy three or four sets of the same clothing.

Clothing—Planning and Executing

- Clothes should be laid out according to what goes on first.

- Avoid clothes that are most difficult for your loved one—such as panty hose, knee-high nylons, tight socks, or high heels.

- Make sure that items are not inside out and that buttons, zips, and fasteners are all undone before handing the clothes to your loved one.

Dressing

Dressing—Know Your Loved One

Initially, your loved may just need verbal cues and instructions on dressing. Please remember to allow them to dress themselves as long as possible to foster an ongoing sense of dignity and independence. As the primary caregiver, you will have to be the judge as to when all caregivers need to begin assisting your loved one with dressing.

Dressing—Communicating and Motivating

- Use short, simple sentences, and provide instruction as needed.

- If your loved one is confused, give instructions in very short steps, such as, "Now put your arm through the sleeve." It may help to use actions to demonstrate these instructions.

- Give praise as justified to accomplishing each step.

- Always smile.

- Speak calmly and gently.

- Do not argue or try to explain "why."

- Remember to ask your loved one if they would like to go to the toilet before getting dressed.

Dressing—Routines and Preferences

- Does your loved one get dressed first thing in the morning—before breakfast or after breakfast?

- Does your loved one change into pajamas right before bed or after dinner?

- Try to maintain your loved one's preferred routine for as long as possible.

- Little things matter. For example, your loved one may like to put on all of their underwear before putting on anything else.

Dressing—Planning and Executing

- Think about privacy. Make sure that blinds or curtains are closed and that no one will walk in and disturb your loved one while they are dressing.

- Make sure the room is warm.

- Hand your loved one a single item at a time.

- Let your loved one get dressed while sitting in a chair that has armrests. This will help them keep their balance.

- If it is helpful, have your loved one use a dressing stick to get a coat or shirt on or off.

- If your loved one wants to put their pants on without help from you, suggest they roll from side to side to get the pants over their hips. They can try doing this while sitting in a chair or lying down on a bed.

- If needed, have your loved one use a button hook to button clothing.

If mistakes are made—for example, by putting something on the wrong way—be tactful, or find a way for both of you to laugh about it.

*NOTE: Wearing several layers of thin clothing rather than one thick layer can be helpful. With layers, your loved one will be able to remove a layer if it gets too warm. Remember that your loved one will get to a point where they are no longer able to tell you if they are too hot or cold, so keep an eye out for signs of discomfort.

Eating

Eating—Know Your Loved One

- Keep long-standing personal preferences in mind when preparing food. However, be aware that your loved one may suddenly develop new food preferences or reject foods that they enjoyed in the past.

- Can your loved one eat independently?

- Does your loved one have a visual impairment that may affect their ability to see their meal or drink? Due to normal changes in our eyesight as we age, eating and dining may offer additional challenges.

Eating—Communicating and Motivating

- Use short, simple sentences, and provide instruction as needed.

- Give your loved one your full attention.

- Always smile, and talk calmly and gently.

- Be guiding, but not controlling.

Eating—Routines and Preferences

- No matter the time of day breakfast, lunch and dinner are served, be consistent every day.

- Offer snacks throughout the day.

- Limit distractions. Serve meals in quiet surroundings, away from the television and other activities.

- Factor into the overall schedule of the day that it may take an hour or longer to finish each meal or snack.

Eating—Planning and Executing

Mealtime and eating can be particularly problematic, and much attention should be paid to ensure success. Below are tips covering several areas to help you with your loved one:

- Use appropriate lighting for each meal.
  - Reduce glare by having your loved one sit with the sunlight behind them.
  - Use overhead lighting that illuminates the entire dining space and makes objects visible, as well as reducing shadows or reflections.

- Create clear visual distinctions between the table, dishes, and food.
    - Use solid colors with no distracting patterns.
    - When pouring a light-colored drink, such as milk, use a dark glass.
    - When pouring a dark-colored drink, such as cola, use a white glass.
    - Avoid clear glasses. They can disappear from view.
    - Use white dishes when eating dark-colored food, and use dark dishes when eating light-colored food.
    - To make dishes easier to find on the table, use a tablecloth or placemats that are the opposite color of the dishes.

Setting the Table

- Have your loved one help in the kitchen and set the table if they are able.

- Set the table as your loved one is used to every day.

- Use a nonskid mat for objects placed on the table.

- Use a plate with a raised lip to prevent food from spilling.

- Use utensils with lightweight, built-up handles.

- Use a long straw with a non-spill cup, or use a plastic mug with a large handle.

If you are new to caregiving for your loved one and they are unable to help or tell you how they set the table, please do the following:

- Set each place setting in the same way for every meal.

  ◦ Place the knife and spoon to the right of the plate.

  ◦ Place the fork and napkin to the left of the plate.

- ○ Place the glass or cup above the plate to the right or left, depending on whether they are left- or right-handed.

- Decide how to set the rest of the table— main dish, side dishes, seasonings, and condiments. Do it the same way each day.

Other Meal Considerations

- Your loved one might not be able to tell if something is too hot to eat or drink. Always test the temperature of foods and beverages before serving.

- Make meals an enjoyable social event, so everyone looks forward to the experience.

- Clean up spills immediately.

- Let your loved one know it is okay to rest their elbows on the table to provide more motion at the wrist and hand.

Meals and Dementia

Eating a meal can be a challenge for your loved one with Lewy body dementia. Here are some simple techniques that can help reduce mealtime issues.

Meal Preparation for Early-Stage
Lewy Body Dementia

If your loved one wants to assist in making a meal:

- Make sure your cabinets are organized with each item labeled with large, easy-to-see labels.

- Use simple, step-by-step written or verbal instructions.

- For safety's sake, you or another caregiver must perform tasks like cutting, which require the use of a sharp knife, or cooking on a stove, or baking in an oven.

- When using a stove top, use the back burners and turn the handles inward toward the back of the stove to avoid any potential grabbing of the pots or pans.

- If you are not there to supervise because you have to go to work:
  - Avoid planning meals that require use of the stove. Your loved one may not remember to turn off the stove and

might not be able to distinguish between a pot that is hot or cold.

- ○ Lay out the ingredients for a meal on the counter or in the refrigerator in labeled containers in the order that your loved one will use them (similar to laying out their clothes at night).

- Transfer bulk items, including milk, from a larger container to smaller containers that are easier to lift and pour.

Meal Preparation for Higher Level of Lewy Body Dementia

- Try to eat all meals seated at a kitchen or dining table or a chair with a serving tray.

- Avoid serving meals in bed if possible. Let the bed be for sleeping.

Activities of daily living can be challenging, but they can be accomplished. Making sure that all caregivers know your loved one, their routine, and the game plan for any activity will help you and your loved one be successful.

Chapter 9

Put Your Mask on First

There will be many challenges to you personally in this caregiving journey that can and will wear you down. As a caregiver, first and foremost, you must take care of yourself in order to be able to assist your loved one. That might be easier said than done, but please make every effort to do so. The following are some general tips for you, the family caregiver:

About You

- Put yourself first (this is not being selfish); if you are not in good physical or mental health you cannot help anyone.

- Arrange some time for yourself.

- Keep a strong support system.

- Do not be afraid to ask for help.

- Keep contact with friends.

- Define priorities; do not try to be all things to all people.

Stress

- Recognize your own stress and take steps to minimize. Stress can be exhibited in multiple ways:
  - Anger
  - Helplessness
  - Embarrassment
  - Grief
  - Depression
  - Isolation
  - Physical illness

Burnout

Burnout for caregivers results from physical and emotional exhaustion.

It is important to realize a family member, spouse or hired caregiver experiences the same emotions as staff in health care facilities, but may not have the needed support system. Suggestions to avoid burnout:

- Know what makes you angry or impatient. Make a list.

- Look for the reason behind behavior.

- Use relaxation techniques, e.g., deep breathing, imagery, and music.

- Ask for help, and accept help when it is offered!

Caregiving is a challenging road with constant twists and turns, from the change in your role/relationship with your loved one, to dealing with the strains of a 24/7 job of caring for that loved one. As much as you may feel like you are alone, please know that you are not. Millions of family caregivers are dealing with the same issues that you are. Do not be embarrassed to share details about what you are experiencing, and do not be afraid to ask for help. There are individuals, organizations, and support groups throughout the country

that are available to you. There is also R.O.S.—
built on the simple mission of our founder's
need to help his mother and father during a
25-year battle with Parkinson's and dementia.
We understand what you are going through,
and we are here to help.

Personal History Form

This is _____'s Personal History

Name: _____

Maiden Name: _____

Date of Birth: _____

Preferred Name: _____

Name and relationship of people completing this history:

_____

_____

_____

What age do you think the person thinks they are?

_____

Do they ask for their spouse/partner but do not recognize them?

_____

Do they look for their children but do not recognize them?

_____

Do they look for their mom? _____

Do they perceive themselves as younger? Please describe.

_____

_____

Describe the "home" they remember. _____

_____

_____

_____

Describe the person's personality prior to the onset of

dementia. _____

_____

_____

What makes the person feel valued? Talents, occupation,

accomplishments, family, etc. _____

_____

_____

What are some favorite items they must always have in

sight or close by? _____

_____

_____

What is their exact morning routine?

_____

_____

_____

_____

What is their exact evening routine?

_____

_____

_____

_____

What type of clothing do they prefer? Do they like to choose their own clothes for the day, or do they prefer to have their clothes laid out for them?

_____

_____

_____

_____

What is their favorite beverage?

_____

What is their favorite food?

_____

What will get them motivated? (Church, friends coming over, going out, etc.)

_____

_____

_____

_____

List significant interests in their life, such as hobbies, recreational activities, job related skills/experiences, military experience, etc.

    - Age 8 to 20:

_____

_____

_____

    - Age 20 to 40:

_____

_____

_____

What is their religious background? (Affiliation, prayer time, symbols, traditions, church/synagogue name, etc. Did they lead any services or sing in the choir?)

_____

_____

_____

What type of music do they enjoy listening to, playing, or singing? Do they have any musical talents?

_____

_____

_____

What is their favorite TV program? Movie?

_____

_____

_____

Did they enjoy reading? Which authors, topics, or genres
do they prefer? Would they listen to audiobooks or
books on tape?

_____

_____

_____

_____

Can they tell the difference between someone on TV and
a real person?

_____

_____

Include names of spouses/partners, dates of marriage,
and other relevant information. (If married more than
once, provide specifics for each partner.)

_____

_____

_____

_____

_____

List distinct characteristics about his/her spouse/partner(s), such as occupations, personality traits, or daily routine.

_____

_____

_____

_____

_____

Do they have children? Be sure to include children both living and deceased. Include names, birth dates and any other relevant information.

_____

_____

_____

_____

_____

Who do they ask for the most? What is their relationship with this person(s)? Describe how that person typically spends their day.

_____

_____

_____

_____

_____

What causes your loved one stress?

_____

_____

_____

_____

What calms them down when they are stressed or
agitated?

_____

_____

_____

_____

Other information that would help bring joy to your loved
one.

_____

_____

_____

_____

_____

_____

_____

_____

_____

About The Authors

Scott Silknitter

Scott Silknitter is the founder of R.O.S. Therapy Systems. He designed and created the R.O.S. Play Therapy™ System, the *How Much Do You Know About* Series of themed activity books, and the R.O.S. *BIG Book*. Starting with a simple backyard project to help his mother and father, Scott has dedicated his life to improving the quality of life for all seniors through meaningful education, entertainment, and activities.

Robert D. Brennan, RN, NHA, MS, CDP

Robert Brennan is a Registered Nurse and Nursing Home Administrator with over 35 years of experience in long-term care. He is a Certified Dementia Practitioner and is Credentialed in Montessori-Based Dementia Programming (MBDP) providing general and Train the Trainer programs. Robert was responsible for the development of an Assisted Living Federation of America (ALFA) "Best of the Best" award-winning program for care of individuals with dementia using MBDP. He currently provides education on dementia and long-term regulatory topics.

Linda Redhead, MS, ACC/EDU

Linda Redhead is a certified Activity Professional and a Certified Activity Consultant with a specialization in education. With a Master's Degree in Art Therapy and over 22 years of activity experience in long-term care in various settings, Linda is a Modular Education Program for Activity Professionals course instructor and was the 2013 MEPAP instructor of the year. Linda is a board member of the National Certification Council for Activity Professionals (NCCAP) Special Projects.

References

1. *The Handbook of Theories on Aging* (Bengtson et al., 2009)
2. *Abnormal Psychology*, Davison and Neale
3. National Certification Council Dementia Practitioners, www.NCCDP.org
4. *Managing Difficult Dementia Behaviors: An A-B-C Approach* by Carrie Steckl
5. *Long-Term Care* (Blasko et al. 2011)
6. "Dementia: Hope through Research," National Institute of Neurological Disorders (201)
7. *Lewy Body Dementia: Information for Patients, Families, and Professionals*, National Institutes of Health; Sept 13.
8. *The Dementias: Hope through Research*. National Institutes of Health; Sept 13.
9. *Understanding Memory Loss*, National Institutes of Health; Sept 13.
10. *Understanding Difficult Behaviors* (Robinson el al., 2007)
11. *The ABCs of Dementia* (Bayles et al., 1995)
12. Heerema, Esther. "Eight Reasons Why Meaningful Activities Are Important for People with Dementia." www.about.com
13. *Validation: The Feil Method* (Feil, 1992)
14. *Activities 101 for the Family Caregiver* (Appler-Worsley, Bradshaw, Silknitter)
15. www.WebMD.com
16. www.caregiver.org

For additional assistance, please contact us at:
www.ROSTherapySystems.com
888-352-9788

14759508R00076